ORS FARM™
SOWS THE SEED

JIM DAVIS

𝆰

RAVETTE BOOKS

This edition first published by Ravette Books Limited 1989

Printed and bound in Great Britain
for Ravette Books Limited,
3 Glenside Estate, Star Road, Partridge Green,
Horsham, West Sussex RH13 8RA
by Cox & Wyman Ltd, Reading

ISBN 1 85304 112 2

© 1987 United Feature Syndicate, Inc.

JIM DAVIS 12-19

JIM DAVIS 1-26

JIM DAVIS 2-1

DOOF

DONK

© 1988 United Feature Syndicate, Inc.

JIM DAVIS 2-29

THOONK

© 1988 United Feature Syndicate, Inc.

JIM DAVIS   3-15

© 1988 United Feature Syndicate, Inc.

SHOOP

© 1988 United Feature Syndicate, Inc.

JIM DAVIS 4-7

FOOF

JIM DAVIS 4-13

© 1988 United Feature Syndicate, Inc.

Other JIM DAVIS books published by Ravette

In this series

Goes Half Hog! 1	£1.95
Goes Half Hog! 2	£1.95
Counts Its Chickens 1	£1.95
Counts Its Chickens 2	£1.95
Rules The Roost 1	£1.95
Rules The Roost 2	£1.95
Feeds The Flock	£1.95

Garfield Pocket books

No. 1	Garfield The Great Lover	£1.95
No. 2	Garfield Why Do You Hate Mondays?	£1.95
No. 3	Garfield Does Pooky Need You?	£1.95
No. 4	Garfield Admit It, Odie's OK!	£1.95
No. 5	Garfield Two's Company	£1.95
No. 6	Garfield What's Cooking?	£1.95
No. 7	Garfield Who's Talking?	£1.95
No. 8	Garfield Strikes Again	£1.95
No. 9	Garfield Here's Looking At You	£1.95
No. 10	Garfield We Love You Too	£1.95
No. 11	Garfield Here We Go Again	£1.95
No. 12	Garfield Life and Lasagne	£1.95
No. 13	Garfield In The Pink	£1.95
No. 14	Garfield Just Good Friends	£1.95
No. 15	Garfield Plays It Again	£1.95
No. 16	Garfield Flying High	£1.95
No. 17	Garfield On Top Of The World	£1.95
No. 18	Garfield Happy Landings	£1.95

All these books are available at your local bookshop or news-agent, or can be ordered direct from the publisher. Just tick the titles you require and fill in the form below. Prices and availability subject to change without notice. A full list of our publications is available. Please send your request to the address below.

Ravette Books Limited, 3 Glenside Estate, Star Road, Partridge Green, Horsham, West Sussex RH13 8RA

Please send a cheque or postal order, and allow the following for postage and packing. UK: 45p for up to two books and 15p for each additional book.

Name ....

Address ....

....